The Giant Sandwich

Written by Julia Jarman
Illustrated by Jonathan Langley

Babs had some butter.

Barney had some bread.

'Let's make a giant sandwich,'
Barney said.

Barney put in eggs.
Babs put in ham.

Barney put in crisps.
Babs put in jam.

Barney put in carrots.
Babs put in cheese.

Barney put in sausages.
Babs put in peas.

Then . . .

they saw a big hand.

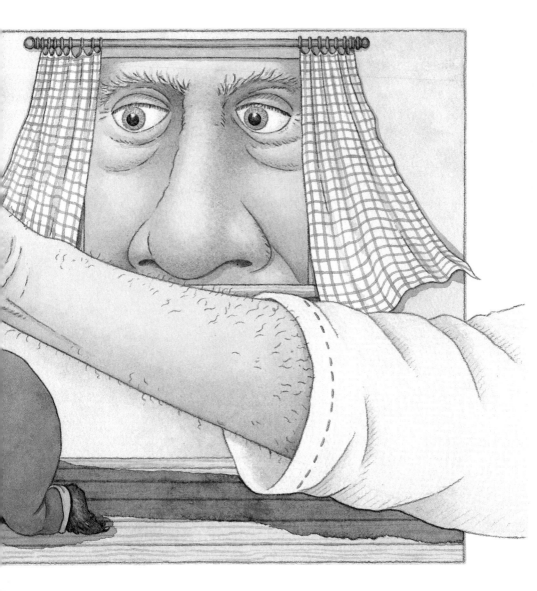

They saw a big head.

'I want my sandwich!'
the giant said.

Babs had some butter.
Barney had some bread.
'Let's make a giant sandwich,'
Barney said.
Barney put in eggs.
Babs put in ham.
Barney put in crisps.
Babs put in jam.
Barney put in carrots.
Babs put in cheese.
Barney put in sausages.
Babs put in peas.
Then . . .
they saw a big hand.
They saw a big head.
'I want my sandwich!' the giant said.